UNFORGETTA[BLE]

PIANO SOLOS

All-Time Pop Hits

Wise Publications
London / New York / Paris / Sydney / Copenhagen / Madrid

Exclusive Distributors:
Music Sales Limited
8/9 Frith Street,
London W1V 5TZ, England.
Music Sales Pty Limited
120 Rothschild Avenue,
Rosebery, NSW 2018,
Australia.

Order No. AM950785
ISBN 0-7119-7054-8
This book © Copyright 1998 by Wise Publications

Music compiled by Peter Evans
Book design by Pearce Marchbank, Studio Twenty, London
Computer layout by Ben May
Cover photograph courtesy of Corbis

Printed in the United Kingdom by
Redwood Books Limited, Trowbridge, Wiltshire.

Your Guarantee of Quality
As publishers, we strive to produce every book to the highest
commercial standards. This book has been carefully designed to
minimise awkward page turns and to make playing from it a real
pleasure. Particular care has been given to specifying acid-free,
neutral-sized paper made from pulps which have not been
elemental chlorine bleached. This pulp is from farmed sustainable
forests and was produced with special regard for the environment.
Throughout, the printing and binding have been planned to ensure a
sturdy, attractive publication which should give years of enjoyment.
If your copy fails to meet our high standards, please inform us
and we will gladly replace it.

Music Sales' complete catalogue describes thousands of titles
and is available in full colour sections by subject, direct from
Music Sales Limited. Please state your areas of interest and
send a cheque/postal order for £1.50 for postage to:
Music Sales Limited, Newmarket Road,
Bury St. Edmunds, Suffolk IP33 3YB.

Visit the Internet Music Shop at
http://www.musicsales.co.uk

A Taste Of Honey

Words by Ric Marlow
Music by Bobby Scott

A Whiter Shade Of Pale

Words & Music by Keith Reid & Gary Brooker

Days Of Wine And Roses

Words by Johnny Mercer
Music by Henry Mancini

For Once In My Life

Words by Ronald Miller
Music by Orlando Murden

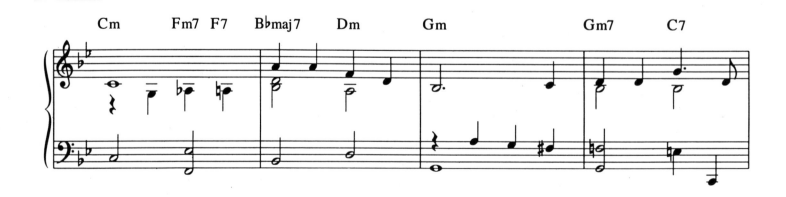

From Both Sides Now

Words & Music by Joni Mitchell

13

Alfie

Music by Burt Bacharach
Lyric by Hal David

15

Girl Talk

Words & Music by Neal Hefti & Bobby Troup

Slow and bluesy

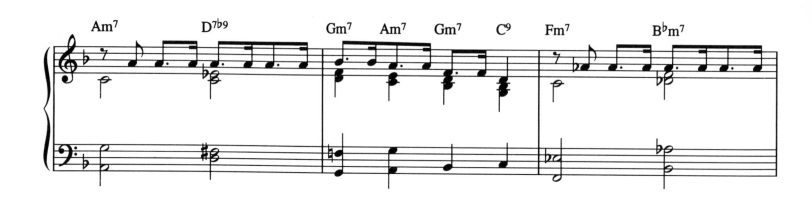

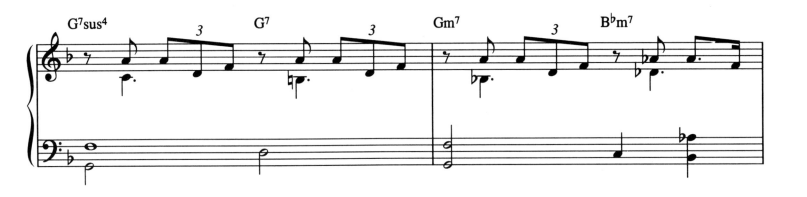

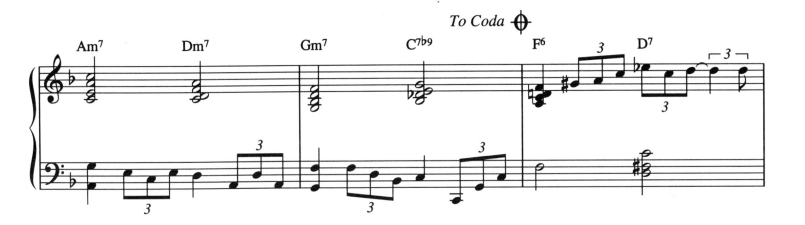

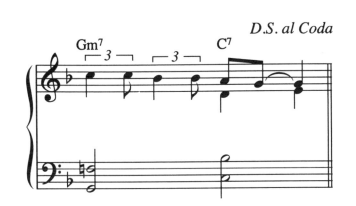

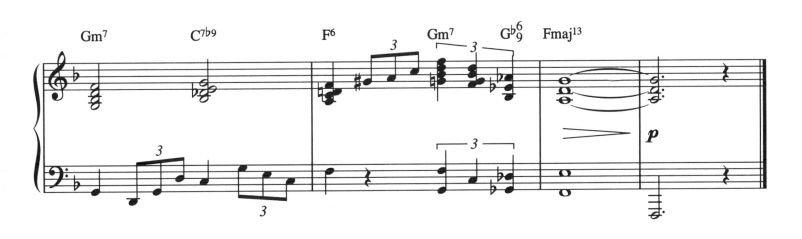

Green, Green Grass Of Home

Words & Music by Curly Putman

Here, There And Everywhere

Words & Music by John Lennon & Paul McCartney

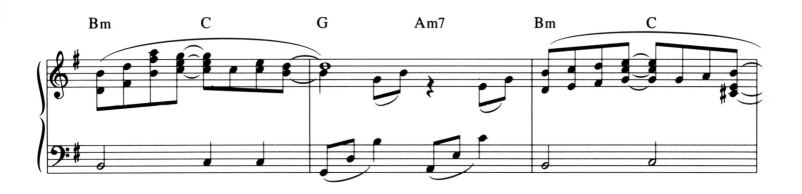

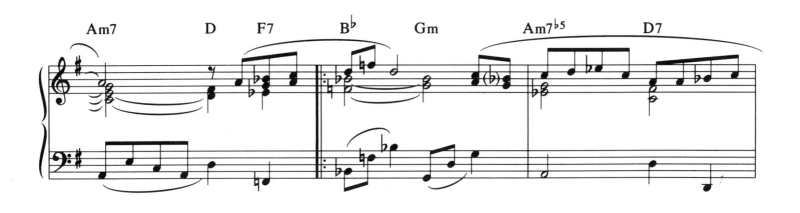

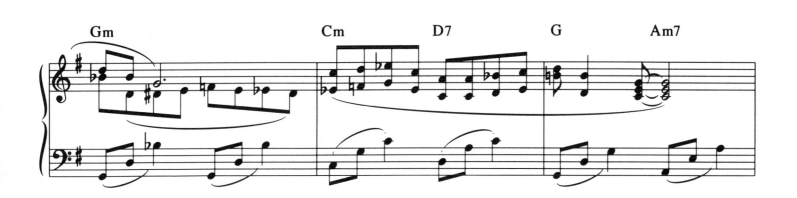

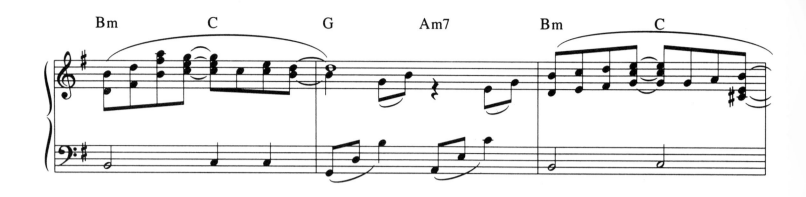

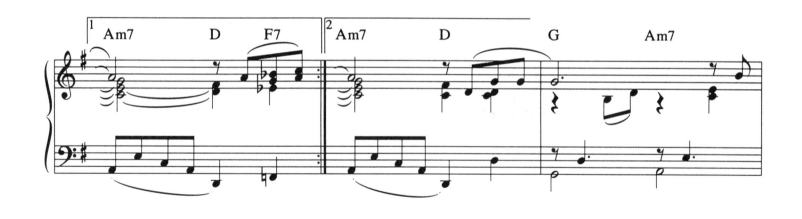

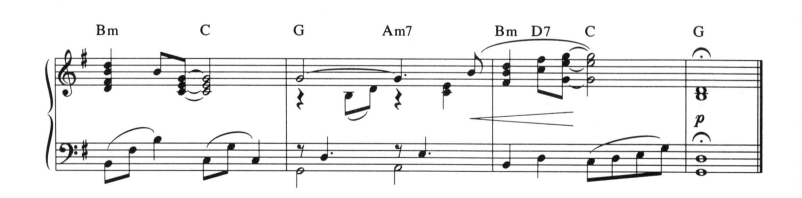

Hey Jude

Words & Music by John Lennon & Paul McCartney

26

Repeat and fade ad lib.

27

It's Impossible (Somos Novios)

Words by Sid Wayne
Music by A. Manzanero

Love Is All Around

Words & Music by Reg Presley

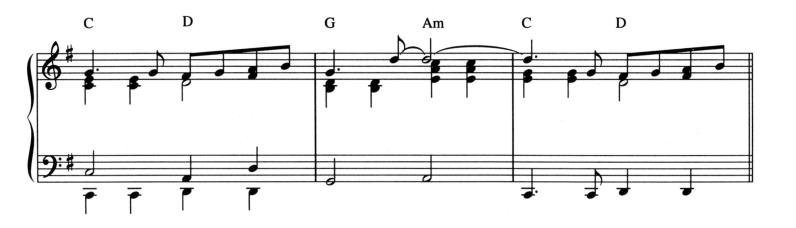

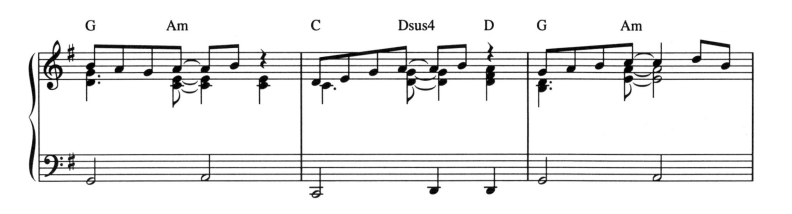

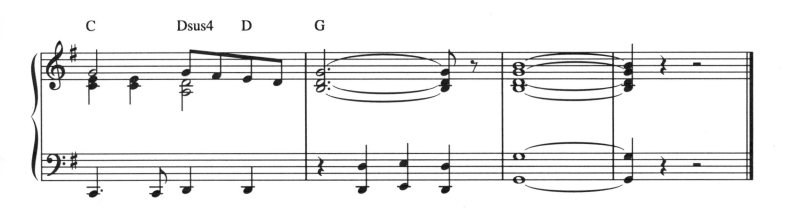

Just The Way You Are

Words & Music by Billy Joel

Medium beat

Michelle

Words & Music by John Lennon & Paul McCartney

Moon River

Music by Henry Mancini
Words by Johnny Mercer

Moderately

My Cherie Amour

Words & Music by Stevie Wonder, Henry Cosby & Sylvia Moy

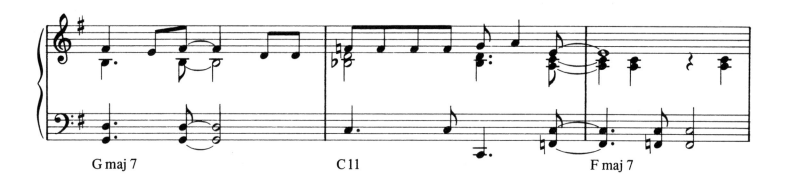

G maj 7   C 11   F maj 7

D 11   C maj 7   D 11

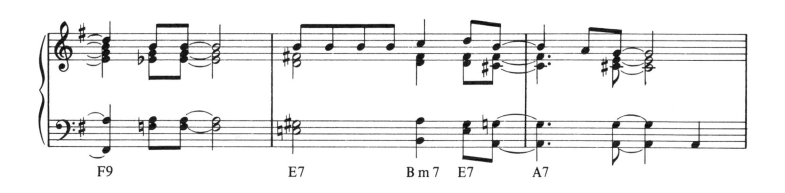

F 9   E 7   B m 7   E 7   A 7

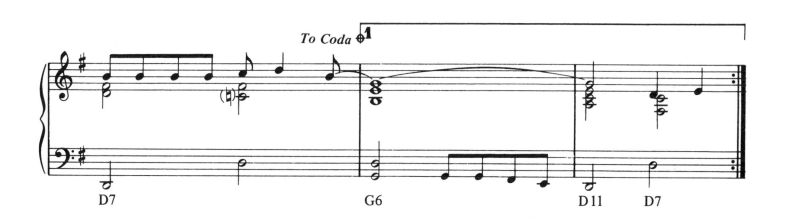

D 7   G 6   D 11   D 7

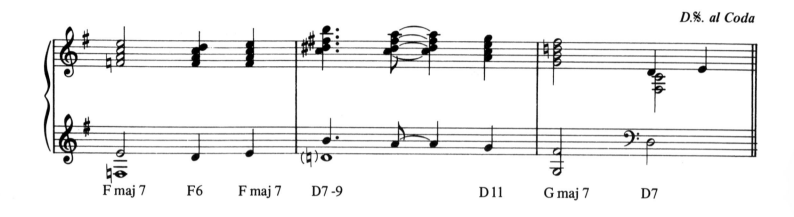

44

Norwegian Wood
Words & Music by John Lennon & Paul McCartney

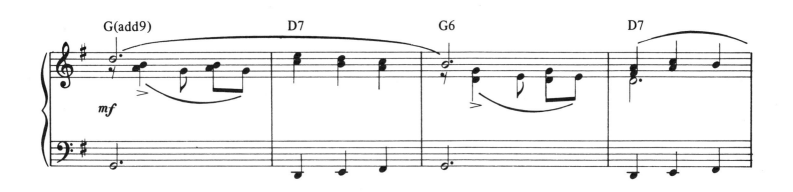

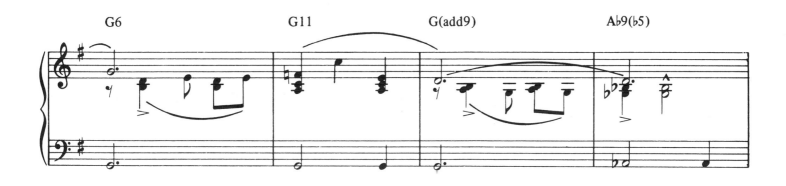

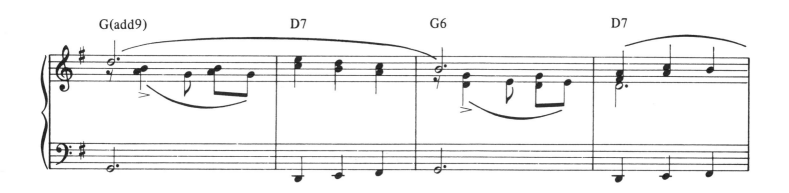

Strangers In The Night

Words by Charles Singleton & Eddie Snyder
Music by Bert Kaempfert

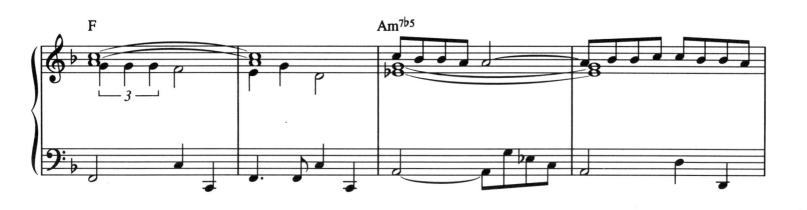

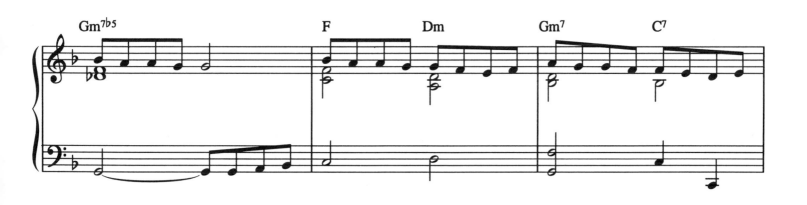

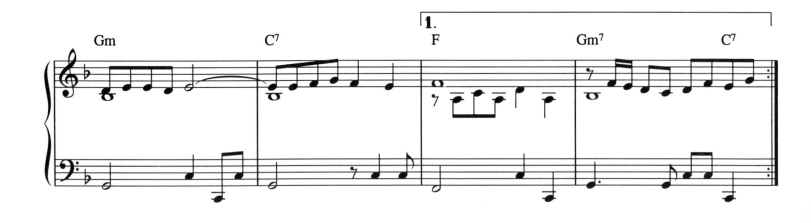

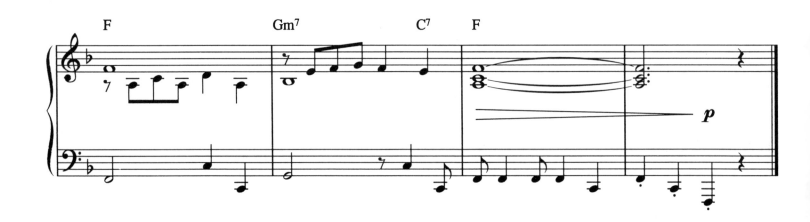

Sunny

Words & Music by Bobby Hebb

The Fifty-Ninth Street Bridge Song (Feelin' Groovy)

Words & Music by Paul Simon

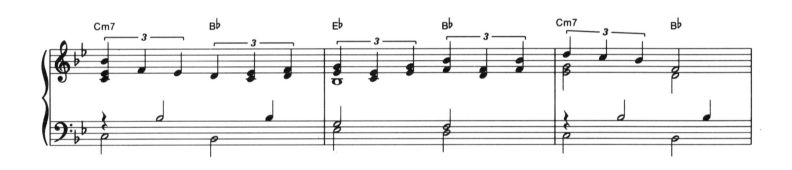

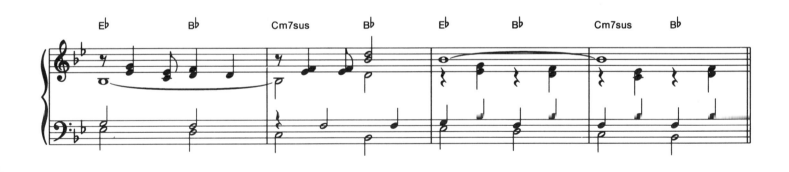

repeat and fade out

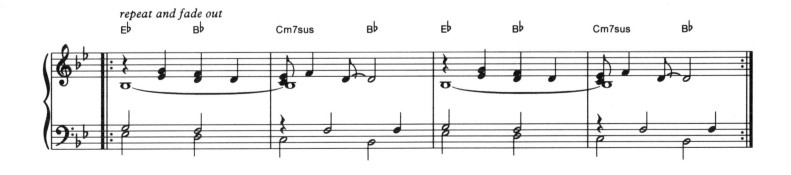

(They Long To Be) Close To You

Words by Hal David
Music by Burt Bacharach

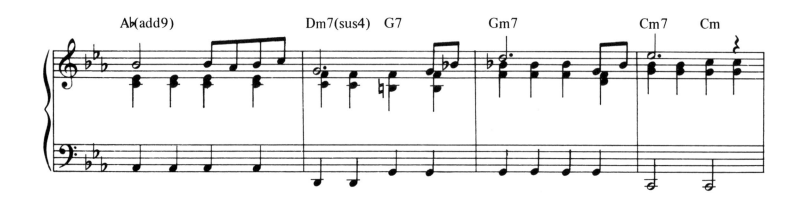

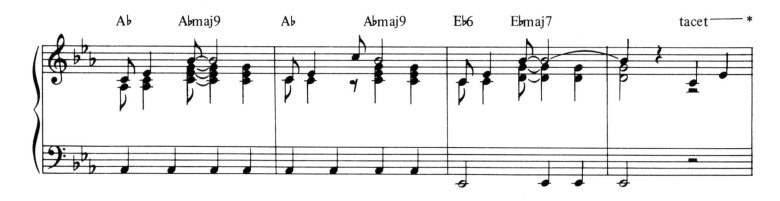

Thank You For The Music

Words & Music by Benny Andersson & Bjorn Ulvaeus

61

62

This Guy's In Love With You

Words by Hal David
Music by Burt Bacharach

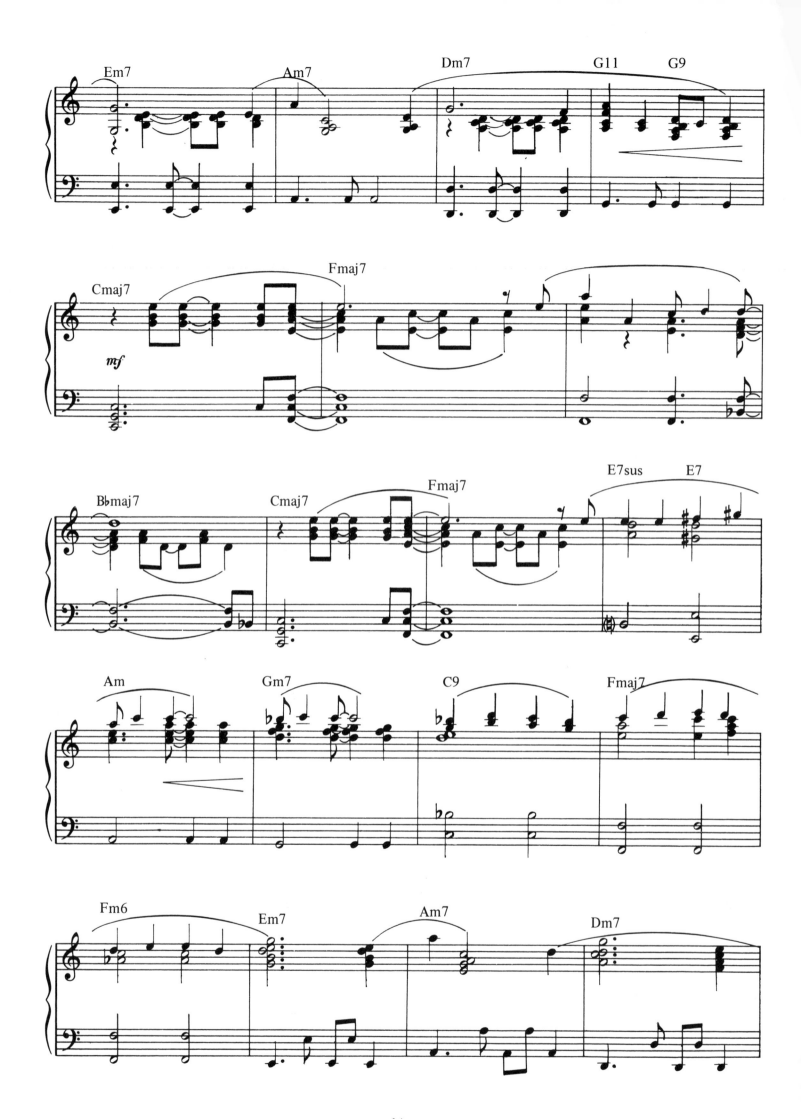

Try A Little Tenderness

Words & Music by Harry Woods, Jimmy Campbell & Reg Connelly

Until It's Time For You To Go

Words & Music by Buffy Sainte-Marie

71

Unchain My Heart

Words & Music by Freddy James & Bobby Sharp

Moderately, with a beat

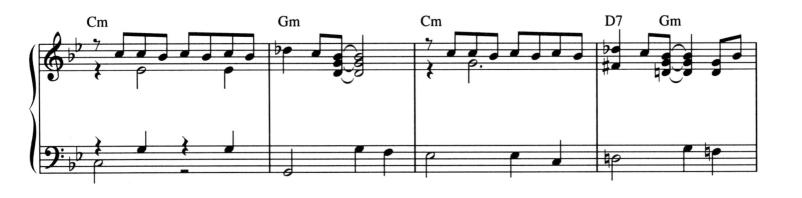

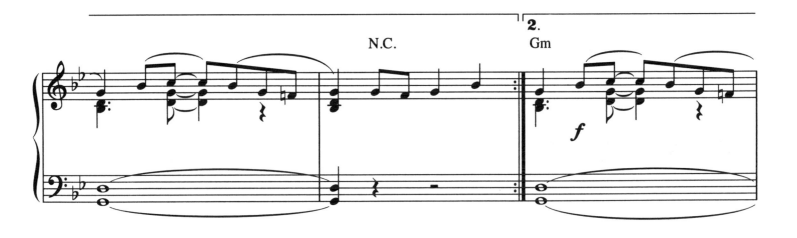

Yesterday

Words & Music by John Lennon & Paul McCartney

Moderately

We've Only Just Begun

Words by Paul Williams
Music by Roger Nichols

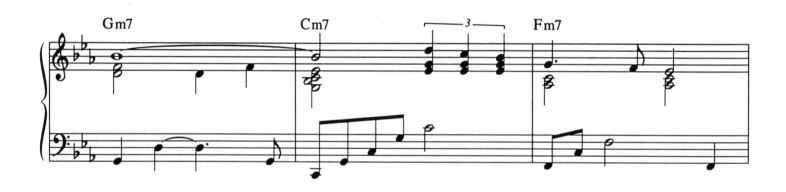